ASIAPAC COMIC SERIES

LIVING 21 SERIES

The Chinese Art of
LEADERSHIP

WRITTEN BY **ADAM SIA** | ILLUSTRATED BY **YAOHUI**

ASIAPAC • SINGAPORE

Publisher
ASIAPAC BOOKS PTE LTD
996 Bendemeer Road #06-08/09
Kallang Basin Industrial Estate
Singapore 339944
Tel: (65) 392 8455
Fax: (65) 392 6455
Email apacbks@singnet.com.sg

Visit us at our Internet home page
www.asiapacbooks.com

First published June 1997

1997 ASIAPAC BOOKS, SINGAPORE
© ISBN 981-3068-56-6

Cover design by Jonathan Yip
Body text in Comic Sans 8pt
Printed in Singapore by Chung Printing

Publisher's Note

The entire human race is fast moving towards the 21st century, an era which will bring new adjustments as well as opportunities. To be equipped for challenges in the new age, it is vital to fortify our minds with powerful and motivational thoughts. *LIVING 21 SERIES* is designed to equip modern readers with the gems of timeless principles for successful and effective living, whether at home, at work or studies.

The next millenium will also witness a fuller impact of the Asian Renaissance, as described by trend forecaster John Naisbitt in his bestselling *MEGATRENDS ASIA*. What better way to be aligned with the emergence of the East than tapping on the vast resources in Chinese culture and heritage.

We would like to thank Adam Sia and Yaohui for the making of this unprecedented volume, and to Dr Charlie In for the foreword. Our thanks, too, to the production team for putting in their best efforts to make this publication possible.

LIVING 21 SERIES
Chinese A.R.T. of Goal Setting
Chinese T.A.C.T.I.C. in Negotiation
Chinese Art of Leadership
Chinese Art of Excellence
Chinese Art of Team Building
Chinese Art of Commitment

About the Cartoonist

Born in Singapore, Yaohui freelances in photography, interior design and illustrations for children's books.

His interest in comic drawings began during his early childhood, when he received encouragement from friends and relatives to enter this line of work.

He is an avid fan of Japanese artist Ryoichi Ikegami and his dream is to produce a volume using his own style of realistic drawings.

Foreword

Dr Charlie In is the President of the Asian Direct Marketing Centre. His expertise lies in the researching of direct marketing techniques that are applicable and effective in the Asia-Pacific environment. A much sought-after consultant, trainer and speaker, he lectures regularly at University of Hull, University of South Australia, Motorola University, Telecom Academy and Singapore Institute of Management.

The Chinese Art of Leadership provides an overview of tried and tested practices of Asian leadership. It is presented in a manner that is simple, light and interesting for both the novice and experienced leaders.

Although leadership is a complex topic and discipline, the artist and writer have managed to bring out the essence of the subject in a form that is insightful and inspiring. The cartoons and short phrases help the reader to go on without the usual fatigue felt in reading other similar materials.

Many readers, especially the younger ones, will find this Asian version of leadership interesting and I am confident that this book will get them motivated in their exploration into the Chinese art of leadership.

For the experienced leader, this book can easily serve as a good reminder and tool for reflection on one's leadership style and behaviour. The framework of leadership provided in this book is easy to understand and remember.

This book contains many ancient Chinese stories that illustrate the various aspects of leadership and their effects. I find them full of wisdom and help to bring up the topic vividly with good substantiation.

I congratulate the writer, cartoonist, editor and the team for putting together this wonderful book. I hope you, the reader, will enjoy the valuable lessons and insights of Chinese leadership which are the "gems" I have found in this book.

Dr Charlie In
Strategist
Direct Consulting Group

Contents

Prologue

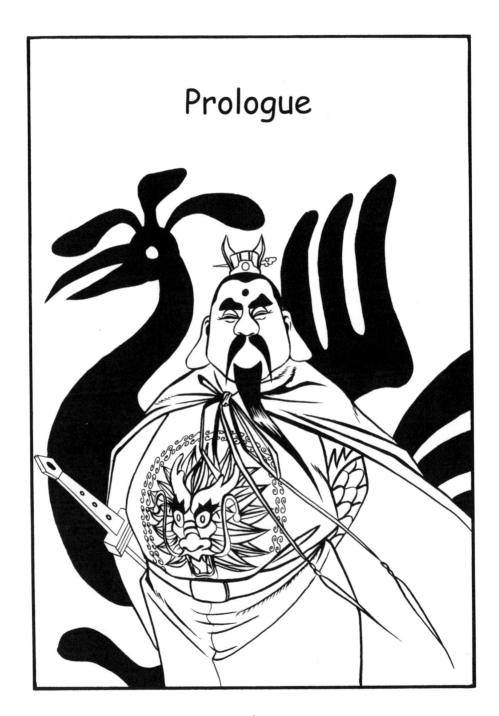

CATEGORY 'A' LEADERS

All leaders can be as common as anyone walking down the street.

They possess something their subjects do not have.

POWER!

BY POWER, WE REFER TO THE AUTHORITY THAT LEADERS HAVE TO EXERT THEIR WILL ON OTHERS.

* 令 means "command".

But this does not mean that followers must definitely feel oppressed.

3

THE NEXT CATEGORY OF LEADERS ARE THOSE WHO HAVE THE...

CATEGORY 'B' LEADERS

...CHARISMA TO ENTICE THEIR UNDERLINGS INTO SUBMISSION.

Such leaders include Japanese cult leader Asahara, business gurus like Tom Peters and Anthony Robbins.

They appeal to their followers through their showmanship and personality.

They may profess to have a highly effective business strategy or a promising alternative spiritual doctrine.

4

They have existed for hundreds of years in the great civilizations of China and India.

The leadership strategies we see today are not new.

The Chinese Art Of Leadership

Please read this passage aloud.

A peek into Chinese

Yes, sir!

A peek into Chinese historical records will reveal a systematic body of work about the philosophies of leadership.

From the benign doctrines of Confucius to the laissez-faire theories of Lao Zi and the legalistic outlook of Han Fei Zi, the schools of thoughts in Chinese history present a myriad of leadership theories that contend with and complement one another.

The following pages present:

7

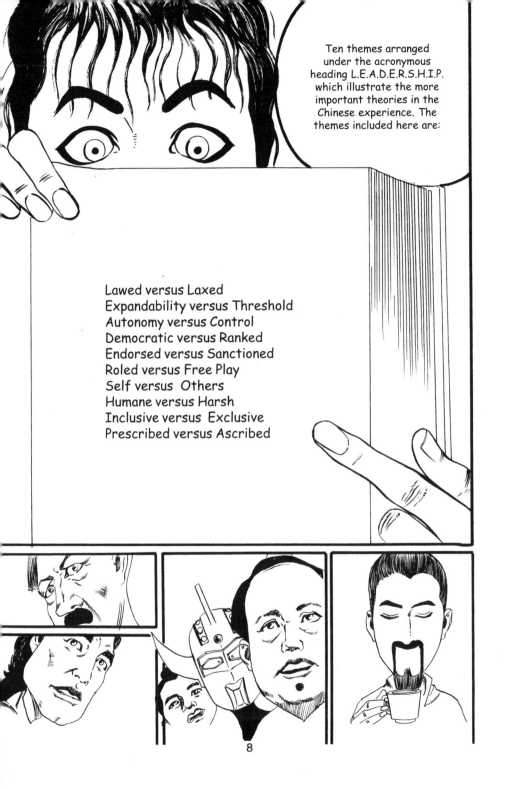

Ten themes arranged under the acronymous heading L.E.A.D.E.R.S.H.I.P. which illustrate the more important theories in the Chinese experience. The themes included here are:

Lawed versus Laxed
Expandability versus Threshold
Autonomy versus Control
Democratic versus Ranked
Endorsed versus Sanctioned
Roled versus Free Play
Self versus Others
Humane versus Harsh
Inclusive versus Exclusive
Prescribed versus Ascribed

Lawed versus Laxed

All organizations have rules. Leaders set rules to identify appropriate behaviour for their subordinates. Rules can help set a direction and also address problems even before they become an issue.

Perhaps no one can better appreciate the use of rules by leaders than the legalists of historical China. The legalists believe that by setting rules and enforcing them, a leader can gain the respect as the enforcer of the rules. But this only works when the leader also respects and abides by these rules.

The Crown Prince is Not Above the Law

King Zhuang of Chu summoned the crown prince for an urgent meeting.

Your Highness is to go to the palace at once.

Prepare my carriage. We must leave at once.

The prince braved the wind and rain.

Finally he arrived at the palace grounds.

But he was stopped at the palace gates.

Alarmed, the prince fled into the palace.

FATHER! PUT THAT GUARD TO DEATH FOR DISRESPECT.

Calm down, my son.

14

Thereafter the guard was given a double promotion.

Laws must not be bent for anyone. Showing favour to a privileged few will stir up animosity among the public and cause them to lose respect for the law.

15

Lead by Example

Confucius said to Zi Lu:

If a ruler behaves with dignity, the people will adhere to the rules without being told.

GUARD A

No swimming

He is doing what he says. Let's do that as well!

The Incompatibility of Yao and Shun's Virtues

Confucius recounted this historical event.

Han Fei Zi said:

When disputes over land use arose, Shun went personally to sow and till among the people of the Li Mountains. Through his mediation, the problem was solved.

Again, when some fishermen fought over territory, Shun fished among them and managed to convince the elders to make mutual concessions.

Shun then travelled to the east where earthenware were made. After the people's interaction with Shun for one year, the quality of their earthenware improved drastically.

To Confucius, Shun's acts were very significant. He lived among the people so they could learn from his example. A sage teaches through moral principles.

But during another time a scholar raised a question.

Where was Yao when Shun was exerting his moral influence?

Yao was sitting on the throne as king.

Rewards and punishments make laws enforceable universally. Shun, instead of persuading Yao to apply his idea through the state administration, went personally to the remotest places. This showed that he was ignorant of state-craft.

It is the same for leaders today. Even today, laws sanctioned by reward and punishment can accomplish many corporate goals. A leader indeed shows ignorance by not enforcing a set of rules and regulations.

Threshold refers to the maximal capacity of a person to do work. Expandability refers to the reserve of energy and resources that can be tapped on. Workers should not be forced to always give the last ounce of their strength.

Lao Zi tells us that nothing stays at equilibrium all the time. Workload will peak and dip. To always work at the brink of the threshold will tire a worker and cause standards to fall. Leaders must know the limits of their subordinates and allow a margin for stretching.

Leaving a Margin for Manoeuvre

Huan He was a sculptor.

27

In every situation, there should be plans for contingency. Allow subordinates to work at a moderate pace so that when it is necessary, there will be reserves to tap on.

A Diffident Governor of Shanfu

One day You Ruo visited Mi Zijian who had taken up the appointment of governor at Shanfu.

But the ancient ruler Shun found time to play the zither and write the South Wind Poem.

Yet his territory was well governed.

You're worried with governing a small place like Shanfu.

An able leader is one who can run an organization smoothly without having to expend all his energy. It is possible to expand one's capacity to perform a task; however, taking too big a leap will leave one exhausted and discouraged.

The Donkey Comes to Guizhou

Originally, there were no donkeys in the province of Guizhou until someone brought in a donkey.

One day a tiger spotted the donkey.

Now, what
is this animal?
I've never seen
it before.

35

Many days passed.

Gradually the tiger got accustomed to the braying of the donkey and decided to venture nearer.

The donkey was enraged and started kicking up a frenzy with its hoofs. The tiger soon discovered the limited skill the donkey had for defending itself.

HO! HO! IS THIS ALL THAT THE MENACING DONKEY CAN DO?

As leaders, there is a need to understand the capacity of one's subordinates. In delegating responsibility, it is necessary to find an appropriate person to do the job — someone who has the devices, in case of contingency, to stretch beyond the normal requirements of the job.

Autonomy versus Control

Autonomy refers to the freedom to make choices and work as an intelligent human being. This basic psychological need differentiates us from machines. Work can become dry when this element is taken away and workers can become irresponsible.

On the other hand, control is not all bad since not everyone is motivated to work. Admonishment can spur a subordinate to put more effort into the work. The bird's-eye view of the leader enables him to spot an imminent problem and take charge to preempt it.

For Zhuang Zi, when the natural is dominated by what is of man, there will be misery and unhappiness. A leader must therefore find the balance, exercising both autonomy and control so that everyone can work towards the corporate goal while finding personal fulfilment.

Four Classes of Rulers

Lao Zi said that there are four classes of rulers, each using different methods to rule the country.

I've heard that we have a king but I don't know who he is or what he has done.

The top class of rulers allow their people to live an undisturbed and carefree life while he applies silent instructions.

The second class of rulers set moral principles and use their office to promote benevolence.

I am convinced that our king is appointed by heaven. That is why everything is running so smoothly.

The third class of rulers threaten their subjects and control them with reward and punishment.

Our ruler keeps a tight rein on us. He's stern and scary!

The fourth class of rulers employ stratagems to outsmart their people and exploit them.

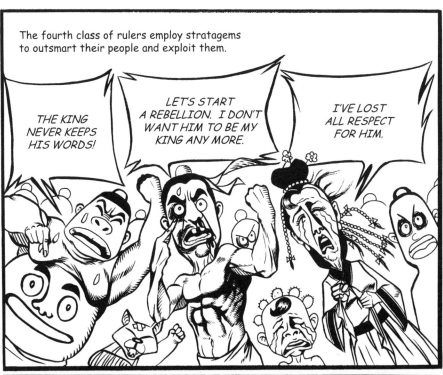

THE KING NEVER KEEPS HIS WORDS!

LET'S START A REBELLION. I DON'T WANT HIM TO BE MY KING ANY MORE.

I'VE LOST ALL RESPECT FOR HIM.

The highest achievement of a leader is being able to lead in an unobtrusive way. Only then can there be clear direction as well as the chance for subordinates to exercise their creativity and take responsibility for their work.

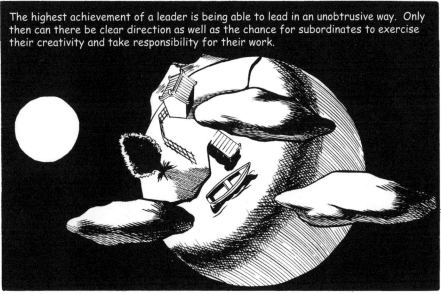

The Death of Two Fools

Here comes a fat sheep heading for slaughter.

A man, brother of a Yan scholar, was journeying to the state of Qin when he met some robbers.

At the point of threat, he remembered his brother's instruction: If you should meet a robber, do not behave like that smart aleck Niu Que.

When Niu Que, the great Confucian scholar, was on his way to the state of Zhao, he was waylaid by robbers.

GIVE US YOUR MONEY!

You fool! You are outnumbered!

Refusing to accept his loss, the younger brother chased the robbers.

GIVE ME MY MONEY AND CLOTHES BACK!

Stop running after us or else...

The robbers threatened the younger brother but he did not take heed. Their patience soon wore out and they killed him too.

Sometimes the opposite action will not yield the opposite result. It is best to let nature take its own course. Results are often not predictable. Sometimes it is more advantageous for a leader not to interrupt the work process with too much control.

The Sea Bird Does Not Like Music

There was a gigantic sea bird called Yuan Ju whose body measured eight feet long. The beautiful phoenix-like bird landed just outside the city one day.

The king had the bird captured and brought to the ancestral hall, where the best music was played and the choicest wine and meat served to the bird.

Despite the king's persuasion, the Yuan Ju did not eat or drink. It starved for three days and died, being too afraid of humans and the strange noises they made.

But I served you nothing but the best. Why won't you eat?

One man's meat is another man's poison. It is the same with the method of doing our job. Dictating exactly what to do often does more harm than good. Give subordinates the leeway to plan their own work. Humans are made intelligent and given creativity for a reason.

Democratic
versus
Ranked

Almost all organizations have a ranking structure. Leaders need power to delegate job responsibilities and function efficiently. However, ranking can also become an obstacle to the essential bonding between superiors and subordinates.

Democracy is allowing everyone in an organization to participate in the decision-making process. Ideas contributed will be assessed and the decision will be made according to support from the majority. However, this process is slow and tedious.

For the legalist, good administration is synonymous with absolute authority as sharing power will weaken control and make it difficult to implement any policy. But Confucius advocates that the people have the right to overthrow a government or authority that is oppressive.

Carriage Driving

How should authority be delegated?

Your question reminds me of carriage driving.

This is because I'm in control of the rein and the whip.

Zao Fu was so adept at carriage driving that he could handle the horses at will.

AND NOW I WILL MAKE A 360-DEGREE TURN.

But if the horses were startled by a pig that suddenly crossed their path, even Zao Fu would lose control of them because his authority had been shaken and challenged by the sudden appearance of the pig.

Then there is another scenario that illustrates weakening of one's authority. Imagine if Wang Liang, another renowned driver, was put into the same carriage as Zao Fu. What do you think will happen?

TURN RIGHT!

NO! TURN LEFT!

They would not get very far.

That is true. Even those who are very skilled will find it difficult to coordinate and work together.

How can a ruler govern a country well if he shares his power with his ministers?

A definite indication of the ranks and status in an organization will clarify the flow of command. This will simplify the administration of responsibilities and eliminate all contending forces. There can only be one head in an organization and jobs must be properly divided among people.

The Difficulty of Doing a Job Without Authority

Premier Le Chi, an envoy to the state of Zhao, had an impressive entourage of a hundred carriages. He appointed a young man to take charge of the carriages.

Halfway through the journey, the train of carriages became chaotic.

Why is the caravan in such disarray? I appointed you only because you seem very capable.

Sir, the management of a caravan depends on more than a capable leader. He needs authority, respect and resources to reward his men.

Those driving the carriages are senior officials. Not only are they older, they also have a higher status. The young cannot lead the old and the inferior cannot guide the superior without authority given to them.

If I were given the proper rank and the right to reward and punish, how will I not manage the caravan well?

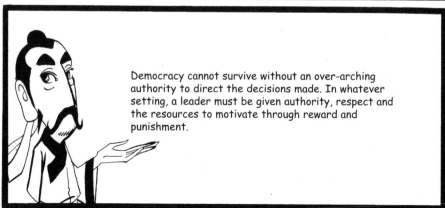

Democracy cannot survive without an over-arching authority to direct the decisions made. In whatever setting, a leader must be given authority, respect and the resources to motivate through reward and punishment.

Killing a Sovereign and Winning Men

One day, King Xuan of Qi asked Mencius:

Is it true that Tang banished Jie, the last king of Xia, and Wu raised an army to smite Zhou, the last king of Shang?

That is correct! The books have records of these.

But Jie and Zhou were both kings while Tang and Wu were their ministers. Are ministers allowed to turn against their sovereign?

Those who cause hurt to the common people are the dregs of society and kings who abuse the just are villains. They are all egotistical tyrants. I've only heard that King Wu killed a man named Zhou. But I haven't heard about anyone killing a king.

Abusive kings miss the real reason for their office. Tang and Wu did a favour for the people by killing the tyrants. They were only exerting the right of the people on their behalf.

When men are coerced into accepting a king, their hearts have not been truly won over. They submit because they do not have enough strength to oppose.

If only I had the strength, I would not have submitted to you.

When men are won by virtue, they submit sincerely and are glad in their hearts.

The king is really the true example of goodness. He is an example I must follow.

Leaders given their appointments are not truly leaders until they win the respect of their subordinates. Qualities like care and concern, sincerity and integrity are surefire ways of winning anyone's admiration.

Reward and punishment are the simplest motivational methods which appeal to the most basic of human instincts. A baby's reward for wailing loudly is a bottle to satisfy its hunger or clean diapers for its bottoms. The carrot and the stick is the most common motivation used to spur us toward accomplishing a task.

The Chinese understand this principle, too. For Han Fei Zi, the legalist, reward and punishment is a central principle he postulates in his work on state management. For him, the most important resource of a leader is the power to mete out punishment and grant reward.

Fangs and Claws

The only reason that people fear the tiger is because of its sharp fangs and menacing claws.

A tiger is powerless when it loses both of these weapons.

Hee! Hee! Ha! You toothless tiger look like a wimp!

In the case of the sovereign, the powers of reward and punishment are the ruler's fangs and claws.

Like a subdued tiger, a king who gives up his authority is at the mercy of the one who gains it.

2 FT

1 FT

When the governor of Wei, Li Kui, wanted every man to shoot well, he issued an order.

Any case of litigation shall be decided by shooting. He who hits the bull's eye with the first try shall be the winner; whoever misses shall be the loser.

This resulted in archery becoming a popular pursuit overnight.

When Wei next clashed with Qin in a battle, Li Kui's troops had a resounding victory because his men were all skilled in archery.

Gain and loss occupies an important place in the mind-set of people. Rewards need not always be tangible; intangible rewards like praise, commendation and approval can be great motivating factors.

The Power of Rewards

Do you think the time is ripe to attack the state of Wu?

Your Majesty, according to my observations, we are ready.

Our people are ready because we consistently reward the commendable handsomely and punish crime severely.

To test my observation, why don't we set fire to a palace building to see the reaction of the people, Your Majesty?

Listen!

Yes! Your Majesty!

Those who risk their life to fight the fire will receive the same reward given to those who died on the battlefield.

This attracted men from everywhere who raced to the scene of the fire with mud and ointment smeared on their skin.

Altogether, the palace was swarmed with 3,000 people on the right and 3,000 people on the left.

Reward and punishment can motivate people to even give away their lives. With ample rewards, a leader can attract people of talents.

Don't cry, dear! Mother will slaughter a pig for you when I get home.

Soon Zheng Zi's wife returned.

Husband, wait!

I was only trying to console the child just now. You don't really have to kill the pig.

Children learn everything from their parents.

Not keeping a promise would amount to teaching him deception.

He will never trust you again if you don't keep your promise. How then can you expect to teach him anything in future?

Like a parent educating a child, a leader must keep his word. The effectiveness of reward and punishment will be undermined if there is no consistency between promise and reward.

Roled versus Free Play

Our identity is closely linked to our position and activities. For this reason, names, titles and roles are very important.

For the School of Names in Chinese philosophy, all interactions and responses are governed by names and titles. It advocates assigning new roles and duties to motivate people to develop skills towards a certain direction.

The Taoists, however, believe that everything should proceed by the natural order. For them, it is easier to find someone to fit into a job than to train a subordinate in a completely new area of responsibility. Leaders should identify talent and allocate jobs and functions according to the strength of each subordinate. This not only reduces stress but also allows subordinates to realize their fullest potentials.

Calabash Seeds

The King of Wei gave me some calabash seeds of the large variety. The tree bore fruit five *dan* in size.

Hui Zi invited Zhuang Zi to his garden.

I had planned to use it to hold liquid, but its wall is too thin to hold the content's weight.

Then I decided to split it into two halves to serve as a basin. But it's too shallow to hold anything. The calabash is bulky and hollow, so I smashed it into pieces.

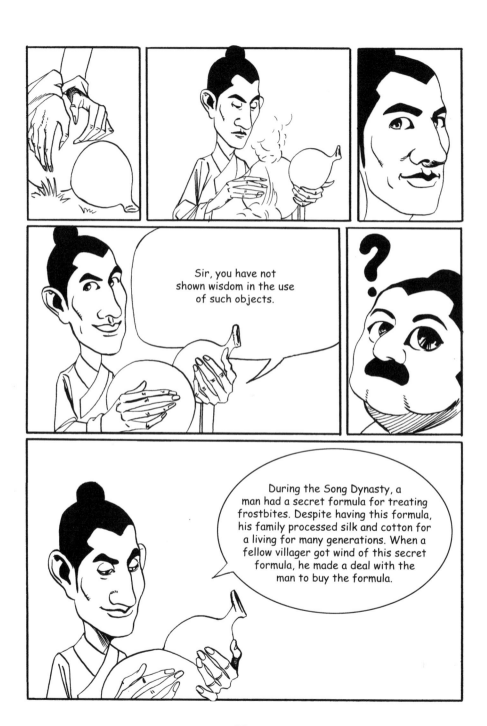

Sir, you have not shown wisdom in the use of such objects.

During the Song Dynasty, a man had a secret formula for treating frostbites. Despite having this formula, his family processed silk and cotton for a living for many generations. When a fellow villager got wind of this secret formula, he made a deal with the man to buy the formula.

81

The shrewd villager took the secret formula and presented it to the King of Wu when there was civil unrest in the state.

Seeing his resourcefulness, the king appointed him General and had him lead his troops to fight against the Yue soldiers.

The formula for treating frostbites enabled the Wu army to successfully rout the Yue army.

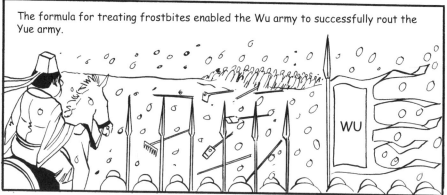

Overjoyed at the news of the victory, the King of Wu awarded a large tract of land to the villager and made him a lord.

You could have used these calabash to make a raft to travel down the lakes. Thinking that it is too thin and shallow shows that you do not have foresight.

Two persons may have the same resources. But one may find innovative ways to use them more efficiently than the other.

Dian Guan Is Punished

Once King Zhao Hou of Han fell asleep while in a drunken stupor.

Brhh! It's chilly. The king must not be exposed to the cold.

Who covered me with this warm shirt?

Dian Guan did, Your Majesty.

SUMMON DIAN GUAN AT ONCE!

公正嚴明*

* Justice and Dignity

Not keeping to one's role in a job will create an anarchic situation. Subordinates must fulfil their basic responsibilities before assuming additional duties. One subordinate taking initiative should not prevent another from doing his job.

Returning a Fortune after a Test

A man named Zhang Xiaoji married the daughter of a rich man.

The rich man also had a son.

Unlike you, my son is good for nothing.

One day, father and son had a heated argument resulting in the son being disowned.

Brother, do you know how to irrigate the fields?

Yes! Try me and you'll see.

Every day, the son watered the vegetable garden and toiled in it. Soon the vegetables sprouted luscious green leaves.

Pleased with this, Xiaoji summoned his brother-in-law.

Well done! Do you know how to manage the barns?

I'm sure I can!

From the son's dedication and
industry at the barn, Xiaoji
could see his change of heart.

So Xiaoji handed all that
his father-in-law had
bequeathed to him back
to his brother-in-law.

Director

New roles come with new responsibilities. While roles help
define the scope of subordinates, they must change and evolve
so that those who take up certain roles can learn and grow.

Self versus Others

Confucius instructed leaders with these words: "Do not treat your underlings in the same manner that you do not want your superiors to treat you." In other words, do unto others only what you would do to yourself. This is called the principle of the measuring square.

In each case, the measuring square for determining conduct is in oneself and not in other things. It is not imposing an external set of values onto someone. Instead, it originates from ourselves. Since every human person has a similar response towards matters, applying the principle of the measuring square gives us an understanding of others. It also helps us to predict reaction to a new set of instructions and take the necessary action to rectify any weakness in it.

The Art of Running a State

Zao Fu was working in the field when out of the horizon appeared a carriage.

Wow! How did he do that?

To drive well, you must understand your horse well. Then you will be able to make it follow your bidding.

Zao Fu was able to control the horse because he understood the horse's feelings and could take the appropriate action. Leaders must be able to put themselves in the shoes of their subordinates. Only then can their instructions be tailored to the needs of the situation.

In the same way, Tang and Wu flourished because they loved the nation.

Jie and Zhou naturally lost their kingdoms because they did not cherish the people.

Cause and effect is a basic principle of the natural order. The way we treat others will affect their reaction to us. To find out about our own performance, we need only to study the responses of others towards us.

Your example must be genuine and your effort enduring. No matter what happens, do not give up.

Although a leader is given authority, he is responsible to win the hearts of the subordinates to create a strong and effective working relationship.

Humane versus Harsh

For the legalist, the best strategy for crime prevention is to implement harsh laws. The main argument against harsh laws is the unpleasantness of punishment. But the legalist tells us that this worry is unfounded since punishment will rarely be used because those under harsh ruling will do their best to avoid breaking the law.

Humane laws are advocated by the Confucian and Mohist schools which teach an ideology of benevolence and universal love. They believe that although punishment is necessary, one should always be gracious and hope for a change of heart. For them, this hope warrants pardon and a second chance.

It is a virtue to forgive. But crime prevention is better than reformation. The modern leader must decide which is appropriate for the situation and his subordinates.

The Valley of Legislation

Dong Anyu was a magistrate of a territory in the state of Zhou. One day, he went on a tour of the highlands with his subordinates.

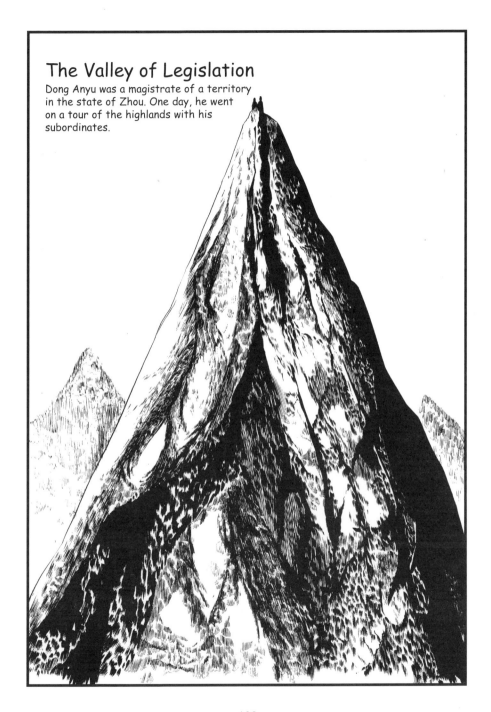

Gradually they came to the edge of a cliff.

Tell me, has anyone ever walked into this gorge below?

No, Sir.

What about a child, a blind, a deaf or an insane person?

No, Sir.

What about beasts? Has any ox, horse, pig or dog ever walked into it?

I don't think so.

Enforcement of the law requires a hard hand; leniency will undermine
its institution and threaten the stability of the organization.

Excessive Compassion Ruins the Law

King Hui of Wei had a talk with Bu Pi.

It is necessary for the leader to be a disciplinarian. There is a time to be soft and compassionate as well as a time to be harsh and strict.

The Nature of Water and Fire

Zi Chan, the premier of Zheng, was on his deathbed when he instructed You Ji.

You will inherit my position after I'm gone. You must remember to run the state strictly.

Yes, Sir...
but why?

It's just like fire which is frightening but really burns very few.

And water...

... which appears soft and mild but has drowned many. You must set strict laws with severe punishment so that none will drown because of your leniency.

But You Ji was too lenient a ruler and the country fell into disarray. Outlaws everywhere were gaining strength so that he had much difficulty trying to maintain law and order.

Sigh! I could have avoided these troubles if I had heeded the advice of the late master.

Harsh laws are justified because few will ever have to bear the punishment since the severity of the law keeps people from doing wrong.

Inclusive versus Exclusive

Rivalry and division are dysfunctional for any organization. The Mohists, therefore, propose an ideology of all-embracing love.

To enhance relationships at work and create an orderly environment, leaders must put in effort to break down all walls and level hierarchical relationships.

Whether out for profit or some special social aim, leaders always deal with people. Real care and concern for a person not only adds zest to the work relationship, but also acts as a real buffer when anger flares up.

Do it yourself! You didn't grow hands for nothing!

If you keep a formal distance from them, they will complain.

115

Bai Lixi's Humility

"Mean and lowly" is not in the vocabulary of Bai Lixi. As a cowherd, he took great care to ensure that his cows enjoyed a living condition that was as good as his.

When Duke Mu of Qin heard about Bai Lixi's lack of airs, he decided to make him the Chief Minister in charge of all the affairs of the state.

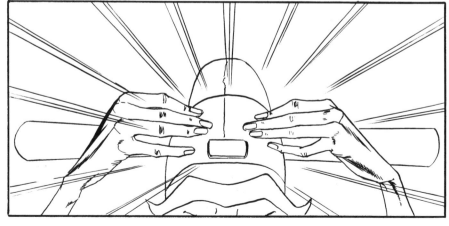

After Bai Lixi assumed his official position, he became a capable administrator. He mingled with the people and the notion of "noble and exalted" never crossed his mind.

Bai Lixi could treat others very well because he did not allow class, status and prestige to hinder relationships. This is important for a leader who desires to gain an accurate view of a situation.

120

Prescribed
versus
Ascribed

There are various kinds of power and authority. The legalist advocates prescribed authority being paid its full due. Hence, the king's word is often taken as law. Such authority derives from the view that the king is divinely appointed, thereby giving it religious justification.

Confucius, on the other hand, feels that the one in authority must demonstrate his worthiness for the position. An emperor who abuses his power with a tyrannical rule must naturally be brought down by a revolt. Today, to have ascribed authority, a leader must earn his subordinate's respect through superior knowledge in administration or the ability to provide resources for the people.

Be Meritocratic

Zhongmou occupies a strategic location. I want a competent man to be its magistrate.

The county of Zhongmou in the state of Jin needed a magistrate. So Duke Ping of Jin consulted Zhao Wu.

In your opinion, whom should I send?

Send the son of Xing Bo, Your Majesty.

Isn't Xing Bo your enemy?

Private feuds should be divorced from official matters.

Who should fill the magistracy of Zhongfu then?

My son, Your Majesty.

Authority should be ascribed to a person on the basis of ability and competence. Efficiency will suffer if authority is relegated according to other criteria like blood lines and social favours.

Partiality? No Way

Guan Zhong was arrested and being escorted from the state of Lu to the state of Qi.

The chief guard, Qi Wu, treated him with great hospitality.

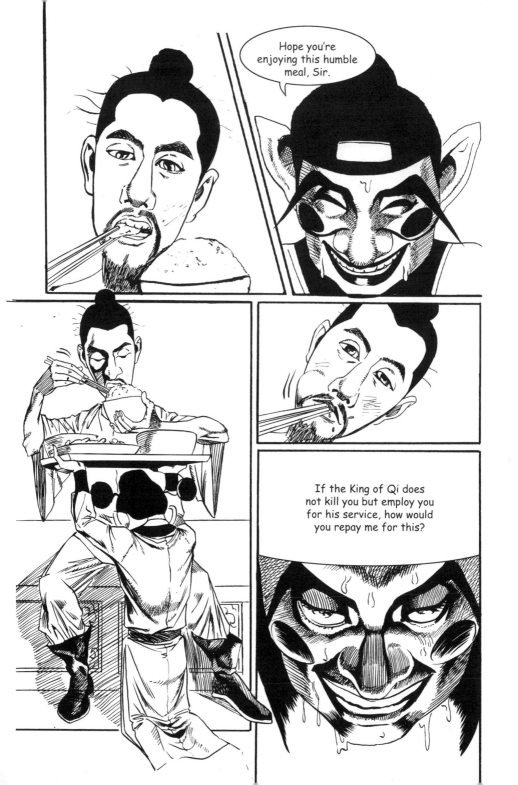

INGRATE!

Guan Zhong's objectivity is admirable. Even when his own welfare is at stake, he held on to his principle of meritocracy. Power and authority must always be conferred according to the lines of competence in order to uphold integrity.

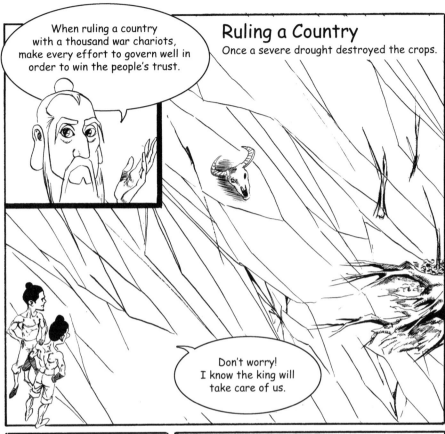

Ruling a Country

Once a severe drought destroyed the crops.

When ruling a country with a thousand war chariots, make every effort to govern well in order to win the people's trust.

Don't worry! I know the king will take care of us.

Exercise economy in spending and show affection for the people.

Ever since the king lowered taxes, we have extras for years even when the harvest is bad.

To maintain one's authority, a leader must justify his position by bringing benefits to the people. Even a king who inherits his throne will not last if he oppresses the people.

Conclusion

Two main features of leadership have been covered in this book. The first describes various styles of leadership and the second illustrates the characteristics of a good leader.

The former lists autocracy, democracy and laissez-faire as possible styles of leadership. Each leader must identify the style that he currently employs and incorporate the positive elements of other styles to become an effective leader. The second speaks about a genuine concern for one's subordinates, humility and a sense of camaraderie. These are healthy traits and the secret behind successful leader-subordinate relationships.

Strategy & Leadership Series by Wang Xuanming

Thirty-six Stratagems: Secret Art of War
Translated by Koh Kok Kiang (cartoons) &
Liu Yi (text of the stratagems)
   A Chinese military classic which emphasizes deceptive schemes to achieve military objectives. It has attracted the attention of military authorities and general readers alike.

Six Strategies for War: The Practice of Effective Leadership
Translated by Alan Chong
   A powerful book for rulers, administrators and leaders, it covers critical areas in management and warfare including: how to recruit talents and manage the state; how to beat the enemy and build an empire; how to lead wisely; and how to manoeuvre brilliantly.

Gems of Chinese Wisdom: Mastering the Art of Leadership
Translated by Leong Weng Kam
   Wise up with this delightful collection of tales and anecdotes on the wisdom of great men and women in Chinese history, including Confucius, Meng Changjun and Gou Jian.

Three Strategies of Huang Shi Gong: The Art of Government
Translated by Alan Chong
   Reputedly one of man's oldest monograph on military strategy, it unmasks the secrets behind brilliant military manoeuvres, clever deployment and control of subordinates, and effective government.

100 Strategies of War: Brilliant Tactics in Action
Translated by Yeo Ai Hoon
   The book captures the essence of extensive military knowledge and practice, and explores the use of psychology in warfare, the importance of building diplomatic relations with the enemy's neighbours, the use of espionage and reconnaissance, etc.

Latest Titles in
Strategy & Leadership Series

Chinese Business Strategies

The Chinese are known for being shrewd businessmen able to thrive under the toughest market conditions. The secret of their success lies in 10 time-tested principles of Chinese entrepreneurship.

This book offers readers 30 real-life, ancient case studies with comments on their application in the context of modern business.

Sixteen Strategies of Zhuge Liang

Zhuge Liang, the legendary statesman and military commander during the Three Kingdoms Period, is the epitome of wisdom.

Well-grounded in military principles of Sun Zi and other masters before him, he excelled in applying them in state administration and his own innovations, thus winning many spectacular victories with his uncanny anticipation of enemy moves.

SPECIAL OFFER

Strategy & Leadership Series

☐ Chinese Business Strategies
☐ Three Strategies of Huang Shi Gong
☐ Six Strategies for War
☐ Sixteen Strategies of Zhuge Liang
☐ Thirty-six Stratagems
☐ 100 Strategies of War
☐ Gems of Chinese Wisdom

Make your subscription for any 5 volumes or more of this comic series (tick box) and enjoy **20% discount**.
Original Price: S$15.90 per volume (*exclusive* of GST)
Offer at special discount (*inclusive of* postage):-

	5 Volumes	6 Volumes	7 Volumes
Singapore	68.30	82.20	95.30
Malaysia	71.60	88.30	101.00
International-by sea mail	78.60	100.30	113.00

* All Prices in Singapore Dollars. 3% GST charge for local orders.

I wish to subscribe for the above-mentioned titles

at the nett price of **S$**_____ (*inclusive of* postage)

☐ **For Singapore orders only:**
Enclosed is my postal order/money order/cheque/ for **S$** _____

(No.: _____.)

For Singapore/Malaysia/International orders:

☐ Credit card. Please charge the amount of SIN$_____ to my credit card

VISA ☐   Card No. _____ Card Holder's Name _____

MASTER ☐   Expiry Date_____ Order Date_____ Signature _____

Name _____

Address _____

_____ **Tel** _____

Send to: **ASIAPAC BOOKS PTE LTD** 996 Bendemeer Road #06-08/09 Kallang Basin
Industrial Estate Singapore 339944 Tel: (65) 392 8455 Fax: (65) 392 6455
Note:
For this offer of 20% discount, there is no restriction on the titles ordered, that is, you may order any 5 or more of the series. Prices are subject to change without prior notice.